Look for a lovely thing and you will find it,
It is not far—
It never will be far

D̶e̶... Lapland
A u...orn's horn ...Bombay
A u...orn's horn
From the Land of Cathay

Oh, he had a cutlass that swung at his thigh
And he had a parrot called Pepperkin Pye,
And a zigzaggy scar at the end of his eye
Had Pirate Don Durk of Dowdee

Her lawn looks like a meadow,
And if she mows the place,
She leaves the clover standing
And the Queen Anne's lace

Did you ever hear of a thing like that?
Oh, what a proud, mysterious cat.

The fog comes
on little cat feet

The Owl and the Pussy-cat went to sea
In a beautiful pea-green boat

Mary Edith Redus

THE FIRST BOOK OF POETRY

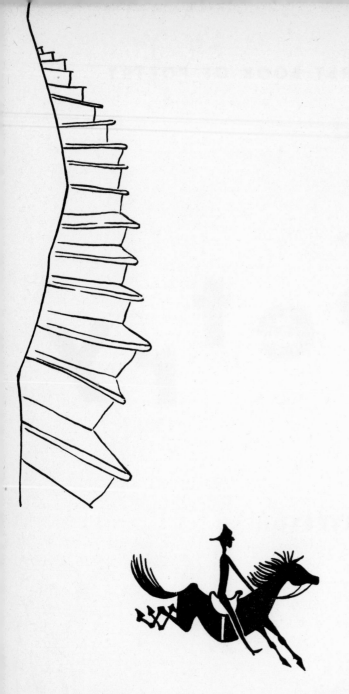

pictures by

KATHLEEN ELGIN

Franklin Watts, Inc.   699 Madison Avenue, New York 21

the first

book *of*

poetry

selected by

ISABEL J. PETERSON

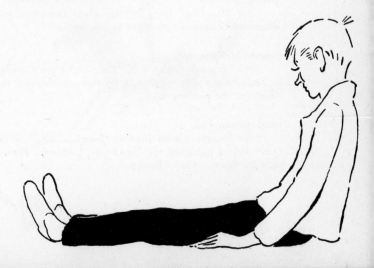

acknowledgments

The poems reprinted in this anthology are used by permission and special arrangements with the proprietors of their respective copyrights, who are listed below. The compiler's and publisher's thanks to all who helped make this collection possible.

Appleton-Century-Crofts, Inc.
for John Kendrick Bangs, "The Little Elf" from *St. Nicholas Book of Verse*, Copyright 1923 by The Century Company. Reprinted by permission of the publishers, Appleton-Century-Crofts, Inc.
for Oliver Herford, "The Elf and the Dormouse" from *Artful Antics*. Reprinted by permission of the publishers.

Brandt & Brandt
for Rosemary and Stephen Vincent Benét, "Christopher Columbus" from *A Book of Americans*, published by Rinehart & Company, Inc., Copyright 1933 by Rosemary and Stephen Vincent Benét.
for Edna St. Vincent Millay, "Afternoon on a Hill" from *Renascence and Other Poems*, published by Harper & Brothers, Copyright 1917, 1945, by Edna St. Vincent Millay; for "Portrait by a Neighbor" from *A Few Figs from Thistles*, published by Harper & Brothers, Copyright 1920, 1948 by Edna St. Vincent Millay; for "Wonder Where," lines from "From a Very Little Sphinx," from *Poems Selected for Young People*, published by Harper & Brothers, Copyright 1923, 1951 by Edna St. Vincent Millay.

Marchette Chute
for "My Dog" from *Rhymes about Ourselves*, published 1932 by The Macmillan Company. Copyright by the author.

Coward-McCann, Inc.
for Elizabeth Coatsworth, "Counters" from *Compass Rose*, in the *Songs of Today Series*, Copyright 1929 by Coward-McCann, Inc. Reprinted by permission of the publishers.

Curtis Brown, Ltd.
for Beatrice Curtis Brown, "Jonathan Bing" from *Jonathan Bing and Other Verses*, published 1936 by Oxford University Press of New York, Copyright by Beatrice Curtis Brown.

Katherine R. O'Hare
for "Mockery" published 1920 by *Poetry*. Reprinted by permission of author and publisher.

Arthur S. Pederson
for Rachel Field, "Roads" and "A Summer Morning" from *The Pointed People*, Copyright 1930 by The Macmillan Company.

Plays and *Child Life Magazine*
for Aileen Fisher, "The Snowman's Resolution" from *Child Life Magazine*, Copyright 1930, and *Holiday Programs for Boys and Girls* by Aileen Fisher, published by Plays, Inc.

Hamilton Richards and *Child Life Magazine*
for Laura E. Richards, "Antonio" from *Child Life Magazine*, Copyright 1936.

Marion Plew Ruckel and *Child Life Magazine*
for Mildred Plew Meigs, "Abraham Lincoln" and "The Pirate Don Durk of Dowdee" from *Child Life Magazine*, Copyright 1923.

Charles Scribner's Sons
for Kenneth Grahame, "Ducks' Ditty" from *The Wind in the Willows*, Copyright 1908, 1935 by Charles Scribner's Sons. Used by permission of the publishers.
for Robert Louis Stevenson, "Escape at Bedtime," "From a Railway Carriage," "My Shadow," and "The Swing" from *A Child's Garden of Verses*.

The Society of Authors, London
for Canadian rights for Rose Fyleman, "Mice," from *Fifty-one New Nursery Rhymes;* for "Fairies," "Have You Watched the Fairies?" and "Yesterday in Oxford Street" from *Fairies and Chimneys*.

Nancy Byrd Turner and *Child Life Magazine*
for "Washington" from *Child Life Magazine*, Copyright 1932.

The Viking Press, Inc.
for Elizabeth Madox Roberts, "The Rabbit" and "The Hens" from *Under the Tree*, Copyright 1922 by B. W. Huebsch, Inc., 1950 by Ivor S. Roberts. Reprinted by permission of The Viking Press, Inc.

Wilson, Dixie and *Child Life Magazine*
for "The Mist and All" from *Child Life Magazine*, Copyright 1924.

ABOUT POETRY

Poems are fun; and here is a collection chosen especially for you, from the favorites of hundreds of other boys and girls. They enjoyed them, and you will, too.

One of the nicest things about poems is this: the more you read them the better you like them. A good poem never wears out. You can read it again and again and never grow tired of it. And all the while, ever so quietly, little portions of it are tucking themselves away in corners of your mind. When you least expect it, out they pop. Suddenly, one gray, foggy morning, as you look at the drifting swirls of dampness, you find yourself thinking with the poet Carl Sandburg:

> The fog comes
> on little cat feet.
>
> It sits looking
> over harbor and city . . .

Or on that wonderful autumn day when the first snow falls, you look at the snowflakes and think of "veils of white lace."

For poetry has a way of making you see things you took for granted as if they were entirely new. With good poems stored away in your mind, you'll find that the world becomes a little more exciting than it ever was before.

There is laughter, too, in the rhyming words of some verse. Try this:

> Once there was an elephant
> Who tried to use the telephant—
> No! No! I mean an elephone
> Who tried to use the telephone—

Or say this one:

> Antonio, Antonio
> Was tired of living alonio

Don't you want to read the rest of these two verses, and find out what happened?

Poems are like songs. There are all kinds, but there is music in every one, in the lilt and swing of its words. That is why poetry is fun to read to yourself, but ever so much more fun to read aloud with someone else.

Here is a book that has all kinds of poems—something for everyone, no matter what his taste. Read them, and share them, and have a wonderful time with them, as many children who have liked them through the years have already done.

CONTENTS

2
interesting people

3
journeying far and wide

4

the land of make-believe

5

the world around us

6

from season to season

7

just for fun

1

a variety of
animals

THE PASTURE

ROBERT FROST

I'm going out to clean the pasture spring;
I'll only stop to rake the leaves away
(And wait to watch the water clear, I may):
I sha'n't be gone long.—You come too.

I'm going out to fetch the little calf
That's standing by the mother. It's so young
It totters when she licks it with her tongue.
I sha'n't be gone long.—You come too.

CAT

MARY BRITTON MILLER

The black cat yawns,
Opens her jaws,
Stretches her legs,
And shows her claws.

Then she gets up
And stands on four
Long stiff legs
And yawns some more.

She shows her sharp teeth,
She stretches her lip,
Her slice of a tongue
Turns up at the tip.

Lifting herself
On her delicate toes,
She arches her back
As high as it goes.

She lets herself down
With particular care,
And pads away
With her tail in the air.

PUPPY AND I

A . A . M I L N E

I met a man as I went walking;
We got talking,
Man and I.
"Where are you going to, Man?" I said
   (I said to the Man as he went by).
"Down to the village, to get some bread.
   Will you come with me?" "No, not I."

I met a Horse as I went walking;
We got talking,
Horse and I.
"Where are you going to, Horse, to-day?"
   (I said to the Horse as he went by).
"Down to the village to get some hay.
   Will you come with me?" "No, not I."

I met a Woman as I went walking;
We got talking,
Woman and I.
"Where are you going to, Woman, so early?"
   (I said to the Woman as she went by).
"Down to the village to get some barley.
   Will you come with me?" "No, not I."

I met some Rabbits as I went walking;

We got talking,

Rabbits and I.

"Where are you going in your brown fur coats?"

  (I said to the Rabbits as they went by).

"Down to the village to get some oats.

  Will you come with us?" "No, not I."

I met a Puppy as I went walking;

We got talking,

Puppy and I.

"Where are you going this nice fine day?"

  (I said to the Puppy as he went by).

"Up in the hills to roll and play."

  "*I'll* come with you, Puppy," said I.

THE HAIRY DOG

HERBERT ASQUITH

My dog's so furry I've not seen
His face for years and years:
His eyes are buried out of sight,
I only guess his ears.

When people ask me for his breed,
I do not know or care:
He has the beauty of them all
Hidden beneath his hair.

MICE

ROSE FYLEMAN

I think mice
Are rather nice.

Their tails are long,
Their faces small,
They haven't any
Chins at all.
Their ears are pink,
Their teeth are white,
They run about
The house at night.
They nibble things
They shouldn't touch
And no one seems
To like them much.

But *I* think mice
Are nice.

THE RABBIT

ELIZABETH MADOX ROBERTS

When they said the time to hide was mine,
I hid back under a thick grape vine.

And while I was still for the time to pass,
A little gray thing came out of the grass.

He hopped his way through the melon bed
And sat down close by a cabbage head.

He sat down close where I could see,
And his big still eyes looked hard at me,

His big eyes bursting out of the rim,
And I looked back very hard at him.

MISSING

A. A. MILNE

Has anybody seen my mouse?

I opened his box for half a minute,
Just to make sure he was really in it,
And while I was looking, he jumped outside!
I tried to catch him, I tried, I tried. . . .
I think he's somewhere about the house.
Has *anyone* seen my mouse?

Uncle John, have you seen my mouse?

Just a small sort of mouse, a dear little brown one,
He came from the country, he wasn't a town one,
So he'll feel all lonely in a London street;
Why, what could he possibly find to eat?

He must be somewhere. I'll ask Aunt Rose:
Have *you* seen a mouse with a woffelly nose?
Oh, somewhere about—
He's just got out. . . .

Hasn't *anybody* seen my mouse?

THE MYSTERIOUS CAT

VACHEL LINDSAY

I saw a proud, mysterious cat,
I saw a proud, mysterious cat,
Too proud to catch a mouse or rat—
Mew, mew, mew.

But catnip she would eat, and purr,
But catnip she would eat, and purr.
And goldfish she did much prefer—
Mew, mew, mew.

I saw a cat—'twas but a dream,
I saw a cat—'twas but a dream
Who scorned the slave that brought her cream—
Mew, mew, mew.

Unless the slave were dressed in style,
Unless the slave were dressed in style,
And knelt before her all the while—
Mew, mew, mew.

Did you ever hear of a thing like that?
Did you ever hear of a thing like that?
Did you ever hear of a thing like that?

Oh, what a proud, mysterious cat.
Oh, what a proud, mysterious cat.
Oh, what a proud, mysterious cat.
Mew . . . mew . . . mew.

LITTLE CHARLIE CHIPMUNK

HELEN COWLES LECRON

Little Charlie Chipmunk was a *talker*! Mercy me!
He chattered after breakfast and he chattered after tea!
He chattered to his father and he chattered to his mother!
He chattered to his sister and he chattered to his brother!
He chattered till his family was almost driven wild!
Oh, little Charlie Chipmunk was a *very* tiresome child!

DUCKS' DITTY

KENNETH GRAHAME

All along the backwater,
Through the rushes tall,
Ducks are a-dabbling,
Up tails all!

Ducks' tails, drakes' tails,
Yellow feet a-quiver,
Yellow bills all out of sight
Busy in the river!

Slushy green undergrowth
Where the roach swim—
Here we keep our larder,
Cool and full and dim.

Everyone for what he likes!
We like to be
Heads down, tails up,
Dabbling free!

High in the blue above
Swifts whirl and call—
We are down a-dabbling
Up tails all!

FURRY BEAR

A. A. MILNE

If I were a bear,
  And a big bear too,
I shouldn't much care
  If it froze or snew;
I shouldn't much mind
  If it snowed or friz—
I'd be all fur-lined
  With a coat like his!

For I'd have fur boots and a brown fur wrap,
And brown fur knickers and a big fur cap.
I'd have a fur muffle-ruff to cover my jaws,
And brown fur mittens on my big brown paws.
With a big brown furry-down up to my head,
I'd sleep all the winter in a big fur bed.

MY AIREDALE DOG

W. L. MASON

I have a funny Airedale dog,
   He's just about my size,
With such a serious-looking face,
   And eyes that seem so wise.

He looks as if he'd like to laugh,
   But yet his long, straight muzzle
Gives him a kind of solemn look—
   He surely is a puzzle.

And he is just as full of tricks
   As any dog could be,
And we have mighty jolly times
   Because he plays with me,

And never tries to bite or snap;
   He doesn't even whine,—
And that is why my Airedale dog
   Is such a friend of mine.

THE SEA GULL CURVES
HIS WINGS

ELIZABETH COATSWORTH

The sea gull curves his wings,
The sea gull turns his eyes.
Get down into the water, fish!
(If you are wise.)

The sea gull slants his wings,
The sea gull turns his head.
Get down into the water, fish!
(Or you'll be dead.)

THE PLAINT OF THE CAMEL

CHARLES EDWARD CARRYL

Canary-birds feed on sugar and seed,
    Parrots have crackers to crunch;
And, as for the poodles, they tell me the noodles
    Have chickens and cream for their lunch.
        But there's never a question
        About *my* digestion—
        Anything does for me!

Cats, you're aware, can repose in a chair,
    Chickens can roost upon rails;
Puppies are able to sleep in a stable,
    And oysters can slumber in pails.
        But no one supposes
        A poor Camel dozes—
        Any place does for me!

Lambs are enclosed where it's never exposed,
    Coops are constructed for hens;
Kittens are treated to houses well heated,
    And pigs are protected by pens.
        But a Camel comes handy
        Wherever it's sandy—
        Anywhere does for me!

People would laugh if you rode a giraffe,
    Or mounted the back of an ox;
It's nobody's habit to ride on a rabbit,
    Or try to bestraddle a fox.
      But as for a Camel, he's
      Ridden by families—
      Any load does for me!

A snake is as round as a hole in the ground,
    And weasels are wavy and sleek;
And no alligator could ever be straighter
    Than lizards that live in a creek.
      But a Camel's all lumpy
      And bumpy and humpy—
      Any shape does for me!

FORGIVEN

A . A . M I L N E

I found a little beetle, so that Beetle was his name,
And I called him Alexander and he answered just the same.
I put him in a match-box, and I kept him all the day . . .
And Nanny let my beetle out—

Yes, Nanny let my beetle out—

She went and let my beetle out—

And Beetle ran away.

She said she didn't mean it, and I never said she did,
She said she wanted matches and she just took off the lid,
She said that she was sorry, but it's difficult to catch
An excited sort of beetle you've mistaken for a match.

She said that she was sorry, and I really mustn't mind,
As there's lots and lots of beetles which she's certain we
    could find,
If we looked about the garden for the holes where beetles
    hid—
And we'd get another match-box and write BEETLE on the
    lid.

We went to all the places which a beetle might be near,
And we made the sort of noises which a beetle likes to hear,

And I saw a kind of something, and I gave a sort of shout:
"A beetle-house and Alexander Beetle coming out!"

It was Alexander Beetle I'm as certain as can be
And he had a sort of look as if he thought it must be ME,
And he had a sort of look as if he thought he ought to say:
"I'm very very sorry that I tried to run away."

And Nanny's very sorry too for you-know-what-she-did,
And she's writing ALEXANDER very blackly on the lid.
So Nan and Me are friends, because it's difficult to catch
An excited Alexander you've mistaken for a match.

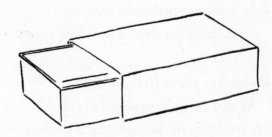

MY DOG

MARCHETTE CHUTE

His nose is short and scrubby;
　His ears hang rather low;
And he always brings the stick back,
　No matter how far you throw.

He gets spanked rather often
　For things he shouldn't do,
Like lying-on-beds, and barking,
　And eating up shoes when they're new.

He always wants to be going
　Where he isn't supposed to go.
He tracks up the house when it's snowing—
　Oh, puppy, I love you so!

THE HENS

ELIZABETH MADOX ROBERTS

The night was coming very fast;
It reached the gate as I ran past.

The pigeons had gone to the tower of the church
And all the hens were on their perch,

Up in the barn, and I thought I heard
A piece of a little purring word.

I stopped inside, waiting and staying,
To try to hear what the hens were saying.

They were asking something, that was plain,
Asking it over and over again.

One of them moved and turned around,
Her feathers made a ruffled sound,

A ruffled sound, like a bushful of birds,
And she said her little asking words.

She pushed her head close into her wing,
But nothing answered anything.

WHO'S IN?

ELIZABETH FLEMING

"The door is shut fast
And everyone's out."
But people don't know
What they're talking about!
Says the fly on the wall,
And the flame on the coals,
And the dog on his rug,
And the mice in their holes,
And the kitten curled up,
And the spiders that spin—
"What, everyone out?
Why, everyone's in!"

2

interesting

people

BEACH FIRE

FRANCES FROST

When the picnic was over,
We sat by the tide
And watched the white-winged
Sea gulls slide

Down the evening wind.
The stars came out
Above the sea,
And Dad gave a shout:

"Oh, wish on that little
Brand-new moon!
Let's build up the fire
With wood from the dune!"

We wished on the moon,
We built up the fire,
We sang, while the sparks
Flew higher, higher,

Like stars of our own
Above the foam,
Till, sleepy, we
And the birds went home.

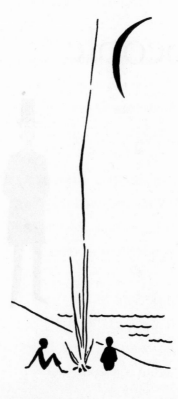

GIPSY JANE

WILLIAM BRIGHTY RANDS

She had corn flowers in her ear
　　As she came up the lane;
"What may be your name, my dear?"
　　"O, sir, Gipsy Jane."

"You are berry-brown, my dear."
　　"That, sir, well may be;
For I live more than half the year,
　　Under tent or tree."

Shine, Sun! blow, Wind!
　　Fall gently, Rain!
The year's declined; be soft and kind,
　　Kind to Gipsy Jane.

PORTRAIT BY A NEIGHBOR

EDNA ST. VINCENT MILLAY

Before she has her floor swept
　　Or her dishes done,
Any day you'll find her
　　A-sunning in the sun!

It's long after midnight
　　Her key's in the lock,
And you never see her chimney smoke
　　Till past ten o'clock!

She digs in her garden
　　With a shovel and a spoon,
She weeds her lazy lettuce
　　By the light of the moon.

She walks up the walk
　　Like a woman in a dream,
She forgets she borrowed butter
　　And pays you back cream!

Her lawn looks like a meadow,
　　And if she mows the place
She leaves the clover standing
　　And the Queen Anne's lace!

TIRED TIM

WALTER DE LA MARE

Poor tired Tim! It's sad for him.
He lags the long bright morning through,
Ever so tired of nothing to do;
He moons and mopes the livelong day,
Nothing to think about, nothing to say;
Up to bed with his candle to creep,
Too tired to yawn, too tired to sleep:
Poor tired Tim! It's sad for him.

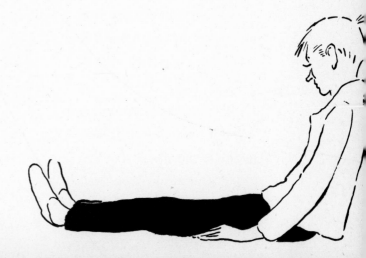

THE SWING

ROBERT LOUIS STEVENSON

How do you like to go up in a swing,
    Up in the air so blue?
Oh, I do think it the pleasantest thing
    Ever a child can do!

Up in the air and over the wall,
    Till I can see so wide,
Rivers and trees and cattle and all
    Over the countryside—

Till I look down on the garden green,
    Down on the roof so brown—
Up in the air I go flying again,
    Up in the air and down!

SAILOR

ELEANOR FARJEON

My sweetheart's a Sailor,
He sails on the sea,
When he comes home
He brings presents for me;
Coral from China,
Silks from Siam,
Parrots and pearls
From Seringapatam,
Silver from Mexico,
Gold from Peru,
Indian feathers
From Kalamazoo,
Scents from Sumatra,
Mantillas from Spain,
A fisherman's float
From the waters of Maine,
Reindeers from Lapland,
Ducks from Bombay,
A unicorn's horn
From the Land of Cathay—
Isn't it lucky
For someone like me
To marry a Sailor
Who sails on the sea!

THE WAGON IN THE BARN

JOHN DRINKWATER

There are mushrooms in the paddock,
  And walnuts on the trees,
And a hive in the corner
  To keep the honey-bees;
There's a hay-rick in the rick-yard,
  And another one of wheat,
And there are cooking apples,
  And other ones to eat.

There are berries on the bushes,
  The yellow ones and red,
There are starlings in the willows,
  And swallows in the shed;
There's a scarecrow in the garden,
  With a patch upon his starn,
But the thing that I like best is
  The wagon in the barn.

For in the rainy weather,
  We all climb up inside,
And we have a team of horses
  To take us for a ride;

And although they think we're playing
   In the barn because it rains,
We go riding in the wagon
   For miles along the lanes.

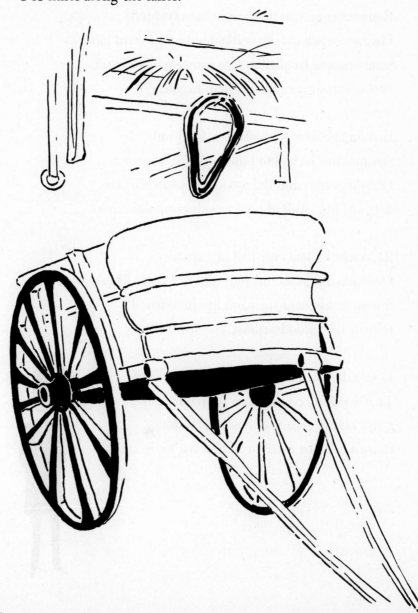

ABRAHAM LINCOLN

MILDRED PLEW MEIGS

Remember he was poor and country-bred;
His face was lined; he walked with awkward gait.
Smart people laughed at him sometimes and said,
"How can so very plain a man be great?"

Remember he was humble, used to toil.
Strong arms he had to build a shack, a fence,
Long legs to tramp the woods, to plow the soil,
A head chuck full of backwoods common sense.

Remember all he ever had he earned.
He walked in time through stately White House doors;
But all he knew of men and life he learned
In little backwoods cabins, country stores.

Remember that his eyes could light with fun;
That wisdom, courage, set his name apart;
But when the rest is duly said and done,
Remember that men loved him for his heart.

WASHINGTON

NANCY BYRD TURNER

He played by the river when he was young,
He raced with rabbits along the hills,
He fished for minnows, and climbed and swung,
And hooted back at the whippoorwills.
Strong and slender and tall he grew—
And then, one morning, the bugles blew.

Over the hills the summons came,
Over the river's shining rim.
He said that the bugles called his name,
He knew that his country needed him,
And he answered, "Coming!" and marched away
For many a night and many a day.

Perhaps when the marches were hot and long
He'd think of the river flowing by,
Or, camping under the winter sky,
Would hear the whippoorwill's far-off song.
At work, at play, and in peace or strife
He loved America all his life!

CHRISTOPHER COLUMBUS
1446?—1506

ROSEMARY AND
STEPHEN VINCENT BENÉT

There are lots of queer things that discoverers do
But his was the queerest, I swear.
He discovered our country in One Four Nine Two
By thinking it couldn't be there.

It wasn't his folly, it wasn't his fault,
For the very best maps of the day
Showed nothing but water, extensive and salt,
On the West, between Spain and Bombay.

There were monsters, of course, every watery mile,
Great krakens with blubbery lips
And sea-serpents smiling a crocodile-smile
As they waited for poor little ships.

There were whirlpools and maelstroms, without any doubt
And tornadoes of lava and ink.
(Which, as nobody yet had been there to find out,
Seems a little bit odd, don't you think?)

But Columbus was bold and Columbus set sail
(Thanks to Queen Isabella, her pelf),
For he said "Though there may be both monster and gale,
I'd like to find out for myself."

And he sailed and he sailed and he *sailed* and he SAILED,
Though his crew would gladly turned round
And, morning and evening, distressfully wailed
"This is running things into the ground!"

But he paid no attention to protest or squall,
This obstinate son of the mast,
And so, in the end, he discovered us all,
Remarking, "Here's India, at last!"

He didn't intend it, he meant to heave to
At Calcutta, Rangoon or Shanghai,
There are many queer things that discoverers do.
But his was the queerest. Oh my!

MY SHADOW

ROBERT LOUIS STEVENSON

I have a little shadow that goes in and out with me,
And what can be the use of him is more than I can see.
He is very, very like me from the heels up to the head;
And I see him jump before me, when I jump into my bed.

The funniest thing about him is the way he likes to grow—
Not at all like proper children, which is always very slow;
For he sometimes shoots up taller like an India-rubber ball,
And he sometimes gets so little that there's none of him at all.

He hasn't got a notion of how children ought to play,
And can only make a fool of me in every sort of way.
He stays so close beside me, he's a coward you can see;
I'd think shame to stick to nursie as that shadow sticks to me!

One morning, very early, before the sun was up,
I rose and found the shining dew on every buttercup;
But my lazy little shadow, like an arrant sleepy-head,
Had stayed at home behind me and was fast asleep in bed.

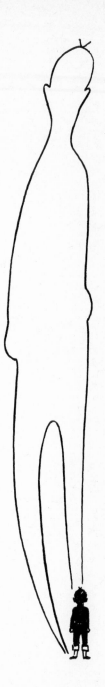

THE LITTLE WHISTLER

FRANCES FROST

My mother whistled softly,
My father whistled bravely,
My brother whistled merrily,
And I tried all day long!
I blew my breath inwards,
I blew my breath outwards,
But all you heard was breath blowing
And not a bit of song!

But today I heard a bluebird,
A happy, young, and new bird,
Whistling in the apple tree—
He'd just discovered how!
Then quick I blew my breath in,
And gay I blew my breath out,
And sudden I blew three wild notes—
And I can whistle now!

BEDTIME

ELEANOR FARJEON

Five minutes, five minutes more, please!
    Let me stay five minutes more!
Can't I just finish the castle
    I'm building here on the floor?
Can't I just finish the story
    I'm reading here in my book?
Can't I just finish this bead-chain—
    It *almost* is finished, look!
Can't I just finish this game, please?
    When a game's once begun
It's a pity never to find out
    Whether you've lost or won.
Can't I just stay five minutes?
    Well, can't I stay just four?
Three minutes, then? two minutes?
    Can't I stay *one* minute more?

3

journeying far and wide

COUNTERS

ELIZABETH COATSWORTH

To think I once saw grocery shops
   With but a casual eye
And fingered figs and apricots
   As one who came to buy!

To think I never dreamed of how
   Bananas swayed in rain,
And often looked at oranges
   Yet never thought of Spain!

And in those wasted days I saw
   No sails above the tea—
For grocery shops were grocery shops,
   Not hemispheres to me!

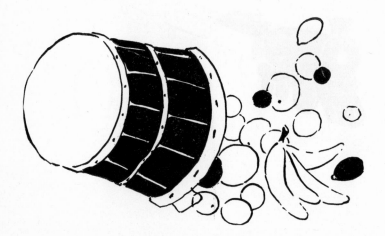

WONDER WHERE

EDNA ST. VINCENT MILLAY

Wonder where this horseshoe went.
Up and down, up and down,
Up and past the monument,
Maybe into town.

Wait a minute. "Horseshoe,
How far have you been?"
Says it's been to Salem
And halfway to Lynn.

Wonder who was in the team.
Wonder what they saw.
Wonder if they passed a bridge—
Bridge with a draw.

Says it went from one bridge
Straight upon another.
Says it took a little girl
Driving with her mother.

FROM A RAILWAY CARRIAGE

ROBERT LOUIS STEVENSON

Faster than fairies, faster than witches,
Bridges and houses, hedges and ditches;
And charging along like troops in a battle
All through the meadows the horses and cattle:
All of the sights of the hill and the plain
Fly as thick as driving rain;
And ever again, in the wink of an eye,
Painted stations whistle by.

Here is a child who clambers and scrambles,—
All by himself and gathering brambles;
Here is a tramp who stands and gazes;
And there is the green for stringing the daisies!
Here is a cart run away in the road
Lumping along with man and load;
And here is a mill, and there is a river:
Each a glimpse and gone for ever!

SEA-FEVER

JOHN MASEFIELD

I must go down to the seas again, to the lonely sea and the
    sky,
And all I ask is a tall ship and a star to steer her by;
And the wheel's kick and the wind's song and the white
    sail's shaking,
And a grey mist on the sea's face, and a grey dawn breaking.

I must go down to the seas again, for the call of the running
    tide
Is a wild call and a clear call that may not be denied;
And all I ask is a windy day with the white clouds flying,
And the flung spray and the blown spume, and the sea-gulls
    crying.

I must go down to the seas again, to the vagrant gypsy life,
To the gull's way and the whale's way where the wind's like
    a whetted knife;
And all I ask is a merry yarn from a laughing fellow-rover,
And quiet sleep and a sweet dream when the long trick's
    over.

AEROPLANE

MARY McB. GREEN

There's a humming in the sky
There's a shining in the sky
Silver wings are flashing by
Silver wings are shining by
Aeroplane
Aeroplane
Flying—high

Silver wings are shining
As it goes gliding by
First it zooms
And it booms
Then it buzzes in the sky
Then its song is just a drumming
A soft little humming
Strumming
Strumming

The wings are very little things
The silver shine is gone
Just a little black speck
Away down the sky
With a soft little strumming
And a far-away humming

Aeroplane
Aeroplane
Gone—by.

ROADS

RACHEL FIELD

A road might lead to anywhere—
    To harbor towns and quays,
Or to a witch's pointed house
    Hidden by bristly trees.
It might lead past the tailor's door,
    Where he sews with needle and thread,
Or by Miss Pim the milliner's,
    With her hats for every head.
It might be a road to a great, dark cave
    With treasure and gold piled high,
Or a road with a mountain tied to its end,
    Blue-humped against the sky.
Oh, a road might lead you anywhere—
    To Mexico or Maine.
But then, it might just fool you, and—
    Lead you back home again!

CITY STREETS AND COUNTRY ROADS

ELEANOR FARJEON

The city has streets—
  But the country has roads.
In the country one meets
  Blue carts with their loads
Of sweet-smelling hay,
  And mangolds, and grain:
Oh, take me away
  To the country again!

In the city one sees,
  Big trams rattle by,
And the breath of the chimneys
  That blot out the sky,
And all down the pavements
  Stiff lamp-posts one sees—
But the country has hedgerows,
  The country has trees.

As sweet as the sun
  In the country is rain:
Oh, take me away
  To the country again!

4

the land
of make-believe

HAVE YOU WATCHED THE FAIRIES?

ROSE FYLEMAN

Have you watched the fairies when the rain is done
Spreading out their little wings to dry them in the sun?
    I have, I have! Isn't it fun?

Have you heard the fairies all among the limes
Singing little fairy tunes to little fairy rhymes?
    I have, I have, lots and lots of times!

Have you seen the fairies dancing in the air,
And dashing off behind the stars to tidy up their hair?
    I have, I have; I've been there!

I KEEP THREE WISHES READY

ANNETTE WYNNE

I keep three wishes ready,
Lest I should chance to meet,
Any day a fairy
Coming down the street.

I'd hate to have to stammer,
Or have to think them out,
For it's very hard to think things up
When a fairy is about.

And I'd hate to lose my wishes,
For fairies fly away,
And perhaps I'd never have a chance
On any other day.

So I keep three wishes ready,
Lest I should chance to meet,
Any day a fairy
Coming down the street.

THE FAIRIES

WILLIAM ALLINGHAM

Up the airy mountain,
   Down the rushy glen,
We daren't go a-hunting
   For fear of little men;
Wee folk, good folk,
   Trooping all together;
Green jacket, red cap,
   And white owl's feather!

Down along the rocky shore
   Some make their home,
They live on crispy pancakes
   Of yellow tide-foam;
Some in the reeds
   Of the black mountain-lake,
With frogs for their watch-dogs,
   All night awake.

High on the hill-top
   The old King sits;
He is now so old and gray
   He's nigh lost his wits.
With a bridge of white mist

Columbkill he crosses
On his stately journeys
　　From Slieveleague to Rosses;
Or going up with music
　　On cold, starry nights,
To sup with the Queen
　　Of the gay Northern Lights.

They stole little Bridget
　　For seven years long;
When she came down again
　　Her friends were all gone.
They took her lightly back,
　　Between the night and morrow;
They thought that she was fast asleep,
　　But she was dead with sorrow.
They have kept her ever since
　　Deep within the lake,
On a bed of flag-leaves,
　　Watching till she wake.

By the craggy hill-side,
　　Through the mosses bare,
They have planted thorn-trees
　　For pleasure here and there.
Is any man so daring

As dig them up in spite,
He shall find their sharpest thorns
In his bed at night.

Up the airy mountain,
Down the rushy glen,
We daren't go a-hunting
For fear of little men;
Wee folk, good folk,
Trooping all together;
Green jacket, red cap,
And white owl's feather!

THE ELF AND THE DORMOUSE

OLIVER HERFORD

Under a toadstool crept a wee Elf,
Out of the rain, to shelter himself.

Under the toadstool, sound asleep,
Sat a big Dormouse all in a heap.

Trembled the wee Elf, frightened, and yet
Fearing to fly away lest he get wet.

To the next shelter—maybe a mile!
Sudden the wee Elf smiled a wee smile.

Tugged till the toadstool toppled in two,
Holding it over him, gayly he flew.

Soon he was safe home, dry as could be.
Soon woke the Dormouse—"Good gracious me!

"Where is my toadstool?" loud he lamented.
—And that's how umbrellas first were invented.

FAIRIES

ROSE FYLEMAN

There are fairies at the bottom of our garden!
 It's not so very, very far away;
You pass the gardener's shed and you just keep straight
  ahead—
 I do so hope they've really come to stay.
There's a little wood, with moss in it and beetles,
 And a little stream that quietly runs through;
You wouldn't think they'd dare to come merry-making
  there—
   Well, they do.

There are fairies at the bottom of our garden!
 They often have a dance on summer nights;
The butterflies and bees make a lovely little breeze,
 And the rabbits stand about and hold the lights.
Did you know that they could sit upon the moonbeams
 And pick a little star to make a fan,
And dance away up there in the middle of the air?
   Well, they can.

There are fairies at the bottom of our garden!
 You cannot think how beautiful they are;
They all stand up and sing when the Fairy Queen and King
 Come gently floating down upon their car.

The King is very proud and *very* handsome;

The Queen—now can you guess who that could be

(She's a little girl all day, but at night she steals away)?

Well—it's Me!

THE SPIDER AND THE FLY

MARY HOWITT

"Will you walk into my parlor?" said the Spider to the Fly,
" 'Tis the prettiest little parlor that ever you did spy;
The way into my parlor is up a winding stair,
And I have many curious things to show when you are
    there."
"Oh no, no," said the little Fly, "to ask me is in vain;
For who goes up your winding stair can ne'er come down
    again."

"I'm sure you must be weary, dear, with soaring up so high;
Will you rest upon my little bed?" said the Spider to the Fly.
"There are pretty curtains drawn around, the sheets are fine
    and thin;
And if you like to rest awhile, I'll snugly tuck you in!"
"Oh no, no," said the little Fly, "for I've often heard it said
They never, never wake again, who sleep upon your bed!"

Said the cunning Spider to the Fly, "Dear friend, what can I
    do
To prove the warm affection I've always felt for you?
I have within my pantry, good store of all that's nice;
I'm sure you're very welcome—will you please to take a
    slice?"
"Oh no, no," said the little Fly, "kind sir, that cannot be,
I've heard what's in your pantry, and I do not wish to see!"

"Sweet creature," said the Spider, "you're witty and you're
    wise;
How handsome are your gauzy wings, how brilliant are your
    eyes!
I have a little looking-glass upon my parlor shelf;
If you'll step in one moment dear, you shall behold your-
    self."
"I thank you, gentle sir," she said, "for what you're pleased
    to say,
And bidding you good-morning now, I'll call another day."

The Spider turned him round about, and went into his den,
For well he knew the silly Fly would soon come back again;
So he wove a subtle web in a little corner sly,
And set his table ready to dine upon the Fly.
Then he came out to his door again, and merrily did sing,
"Come hither, hither, pretty Fly, with the pearl and silver
    wing;
Your robes are green and purple, there's a crest upon your
    head;
Your eyes are like the diamond bright, but mine are dull as
    lead."

Alas, alas! how very soon this silly little Fly,
Hearing his wily, flattering words, came slowly flitting by;
With buzzing wings she hung aloft, then near and nearer
    drew,—
Thinking only of her brilliant eyes, and green and purple
    hue;

Thinking only of her crested head—poor foolish thing! At
    last,
Up jumped the cunning Spider, and fiercely held her fast.
He dragged her up his winding stair, into his dismal den
Within his little parlor—but she ne'er came out again!

And now, dear little children, who may this story read,
To idle, silly, flattering words, I pray you ne'er give heed;
Unto an evil counsellor close heart, and ear, and eye,
And take a lesson from this tale of the Spider and the Fly.

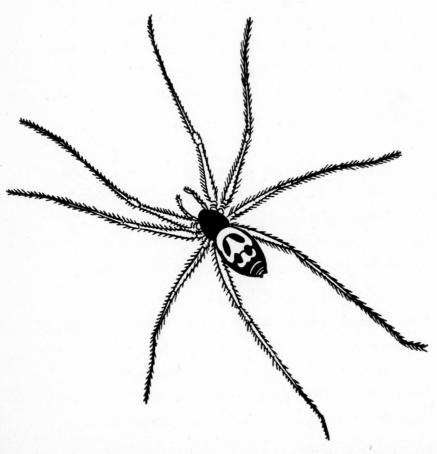

YESTERDAY IN OXFORD STREET

ROSE FYLEMAN

Yesterday in Oxford Street, oh, what d'you think, my dears?
I had the most exciting time I've had for years and years;
The buildings looked so straight and tall, the sky was blue
     between,
And, riding on a motor-bus, I saw the fairy queen!

Sitting there upon the rail and bobbing up and down,
The sun was shining on her wings and on her golden crown;
And looking at the shops she was, the pretty silks and lace—
She seemed to think that Oxford Street was quite a lovely
     place.

And once she turned and looked at me, and waved her little
     hand;
But I could only stare and stare—oh, would she understand?
I simply couldn't speak at all, I simply couldn't stir,
And all the rest of Oxford Street was just a shining blur.

Then suddenly she shook her wings—a bird had fluttered
     by—
And down into the street she looked and up into the sky;
And perching on the railing on a tiny fairy toe,
She flashed away so quickly that I hardly saw her go.

I never saw her any more, altho' I looked all day;

Perhaps she only came to peep, and never meant to stay:

But oh, my dears, just think of it, just think what luck for
me,

That she should come to Oxford Street, and I be there to see!

THE LITTLE ELF

JOHN KENDRICK BANGS

I met a little Elfman once,
Down where the lilies blow.
I asked him why he was so small,
And why he didn't grow.

He slightly frowned, and with his eye
He looked me through and through—
"I'm just as big for me," said he,
"As you are big for you!"

5

the

world around us

THE SUN

JOHN DRINKWATER

I told the Sun that I was glad,
   I'm sure I don't know why;
Somehow the pleasant way he had
   Of shining in the sky,
Just put a notion in my head
   That wouldn't it be fun
If, walking on the hill, I said
   "I'm happy" to the Sun.

NIGHT

SARA TEASDALE

Stars over snow,
　　And in the west a planet
Swinging below a star—
　　Look for a lovely thing and you will find it,
It is not far—
　　It never will be far.

ESCAPE AT BEDTIME

ROBERT LOUIS STEVENSON

The lights from the parlour and kitchen shone out
   Through the blinds and the windows and bars;
And high overhead and all moving about,
   There were thousands of millions of stars.
There ne'er were such thousands of leaves on a tree,
   Nor of people in church or the Park,
As the crowds of the stars that looked down upon me,
   And that glittered and winked in the dark.

The Dog, and the Plough, and the Hunter, and all,
   And the star of the sailor, and Mars,
These shone in the sky, and the pail by the wall
   Would be half full of water and stars.
They saw me at last, and they chased me with cries,
   And they soon had me packed into bed;
But the glory kept shining and bright in my eyes,
   And the stars going round in my head.

CHECK

JAMES STEPHENS

The Night was creeping on the ground!
She crept and did not make a sound,

Until she reached the tree: And then
She covered it, and stole again

Along the grass beside the wall!
—I heard the rustling of her shawl

As she threw blackness everywhere
Along the sky, the ground, the air,

And in the room where I was hid!
But, no matter what she did

To everything that was without,
She could not put my candle out!

So I stared at the Night! And she
Stared back solemnly at me!

A SWING SONG

WILLIAM ALLINGHAM

Swing, swing,
Sing, sing,
Here! my throne and I am a King!
Swing, sing,
Swing, sing,
Farewell, earth, for I'm on the wing!

Low, high,
Here I fly,
Like a bird through sunny sky;
Free, free,
Over the lea,
Over the mountain, over the sea!

Up, down,
Up and down,
Which is the way to London Town?
Where? Where?
Up in the air,
Close your eyes, and now you are there!

Soon, soon,
Afternoon,
Over the sunset, over the moon;

Far, far;
Over all bar,
Sweeping on from star to star!

No, no,
Low, low,
Sweeping daisies with my toe.
Slow, slow,
To and fro,
Slow—
      slow—
            slow—
                slow.

WHO HAS SEEN THE WIND?

CHRISTINA ROSSETTI

Who has seen the wind?
  Neither I nor you:
But when the leaves hang trembling
  The wind is passing thro'.

Who has seen the wind?
  Neither you nor I:
But when the trees bow down their heads
  The wind is passing by.

MORNING

EMILY DICKINSON

Will there really be a morning?
Is there such a thing as day?
Could I see it from the mountains
If I were as tall as they?

Has it feet like water-lilies?
Has it feathers like a bird?
Is it brought from famous countries
Of which I have never heard?

Oh, some scholar! Oh, some sailor!
Oh, some wise man from the skies!
Please to tell a little pilgrim
Where the place called morning lies!

MOCKERY

KATHERINE DIXON RIGGS

Happened that the moon was up before I went to bed,
Poking through the bramble-trees her round, gold head.
I didn't stop for stocking,
I didn't stop for shoe,
But went running out to meet her—oh, the night was blue!

Barefoot down the hill road, dust beneath my toes;
Barefoot in the pasture smelling sweet of fern and rose!
Oh, night was running with me,
Tame folk were all in bed—
And the moon was just showing her wild gold head.

But before I reached the hilltop where the bramble-trees are
   tall,
I looked to see my lady moon—she wasn't there at all!
Not sitting on the hilltop,
Nor slipping through the air,
Nor hanging in the brambles by her bright gold hair!

I walked slowly down the pasture and slowly up the hill,
Wondering and wondering, and very, very still.
I wouldn't look behind me,
I went at once to bed—
And poking through the window was her bold gold head!

MOTHER TO SON

LANGSTON HUGHES

Well, son, I'll tell you:
Life for me ain't been no crystal stair.
It's had tacks in it,
And splinters,
And boards torn up,
And places with no carpet on the floor—
Bare.
But all the time
I'se been a-climbin' on,
And reachin' landin's,
And turnin' corners,
And sometimes goin' in the dark
Where there ain't been no light.
So, boy, don't you turn back.
Don't you set down on the steps
'Cause you find it kinder hard.
Don't you fall now—
For I'se still goin', honey,
I'se still climbin',
And life for me ain't been no crystal stair.

THE FALLING STAR

SARA TEASDALE

I saw a star slide down the sky,
Blinding the north as it went by,
Too burning and too quick to hold,
Too lovely to be bought or sold,
Good only to make wishes on
And then forever to be gone.

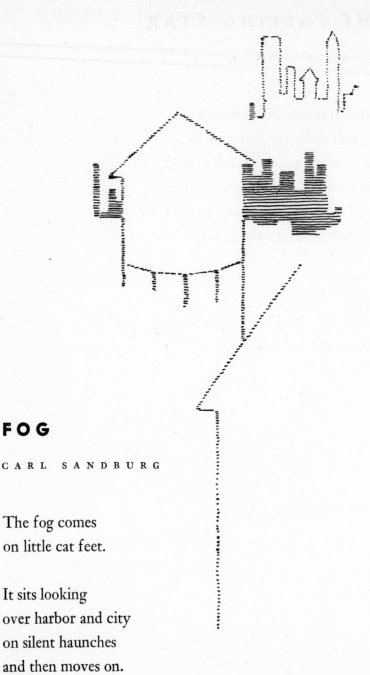

FOG

CARL SANDBURG

The fog comes
on little cat feet.

It sits looking
over harbor and city
on silent haunches
and then moves on.

BOATS SAIL ON THE RIVERS

CHRISTINA ROSSETTI

Boats sail on the rivers,
   And ships sail on the seas;
But clouds that sail across the sky
   Are prettier far than these.

There are bridges on the rivers,
   As pretty as you please;
But the bow that bridges heaven,
   And overtops the trees,
And builds a road from earth to sky,
   Is prettier far than these.

TREES

HARRY BEHN

Trees are the kindest things I know,
They do no harm, they simply grow

And spread a shade for sleepy cows,
And gather birds among their boughs.

They give us fruit in leaves above,
And wood to make our houses of,

And leaves to burn on Hallowe'en,
And in the Spring new buds of green.

They are the first when day's begun
To touch the beams of morning sun,

They are the last to hold the light
When evening changes into night,

And when a moon floats on the sky
They hum a drowsy lullaby

Of sleepy children long ago . . .
Trees are the kindest things I know.

AFTERNOON ON A HILL

EDNA ST. VINCENT MILLAY

I will be the gladdest thing
   Under the sun!
I will touch a hundred flowers
   And not pick one.

I will look at cliffs and clouds
   With quiet eyes,
Watch the wind bow down the grass,
   And the grass rise.

And when lights begin to show
   Up from the town,
I will mark which must be mine,
   And then start down!

THE NIGHT WILL NEVER STAY

ELEANOR FARJEON

The night will never stay,
The night will still go by,
Though with a million stars
You pin it to the sky;
Though you bind it with the blowing wind
And buckle it with the moon,
The night will slip away
Like sorrow or a tune.

6

from

season to season

SLEET STORM

JAMES S. TIPPETT

TIC-TIC-TIC!
The sound of the sleet
Fell like the beat
Of tiny feet,
Racing and chasing down the street:
The quick sharp beat
Of a million hoofs
Clicked and clattered
Across the roofs.
The sleet storm fell
Through a day and a night
With a tic-tic-tic
That was fast and light.

On the second morning
A cold sun shone
On a glittering, crystal,
Frigid zone.
Each bush and branch
Was icily hung
With the frozen song
The sleet had sung.
The branches swayed
With their icy load

Where millions of diamonds
Flashed and glowed.
Steep roofs shone
With a blinding glare.
Fringed with icicles
Everywhere.

But the tic-tic-tic
Of the sleet was still,
Caught on each glistening
Valley and hill.

STOPPING BY WOODS ON A SNOWY EVENING

ROBERT FROST

Whose woods these are I think I know.
His house is in the village though;
He will not see me stopping here
To watch his woods fill up with snow.

My little horse must think it queer
To stop without a farmhouse near
Between the woods and frozen lake
The darkest evening of the year.

He gives his harness bells a shake
To ask if there is some mistake.
The only other sound's the sweep
Of easy wind and downy flake.

The woods are lovely, dark, and deep.
But I have promises to keep,
And miles to go before I sleep,
And miles to go before I sleep.

FALLING SNOW

AUTHOR UNKNOWN

See the pretty snowflakes
   Falling from the sky;
On the walk and housetops
   Soft and thick they lie.

On the window-ledges
   On the branches bare;
Now how fast they gather,
   Filling all the air.

Look into the garden,
   Where the grass was green;
Covered by the snowflakes,
   Not a blade is seen.

Now the bare black bushes
   All look soft and white,
Every twig is laden—
   What a pretty sight!

FEBRUARY TWILIGHT

SARA TEASDALE

I stood beside a hill
   Smooth with new-laid snow,
A single star looked out
   From the cold evening glow.

There was no other creature
   That saw what I could see—
I stood and watched the evening star
   As long as it watched me.

VELVET SHOES

ELINOR WYLIE

Let us walk in the white snow
    In a soundless space;
With footsteps quiet and slow,
    At a tranquil pace,
    Under veils of white lace.

I shall go shod in silk,
    And you in wool,
White as a white cow's milk,
    More beautiful
    Than the breast of a gull.

We shall walk through the still town
    In a windless peace;
We shall step upon white down,
    Upon silver fleece,
    Upon softer than these.

We shall walk in velvet shoes:
    Wherever we go
Silence will fall like dews
    On white silence below.
    We shall walk in the snow.

THE SNOWMAN'S RESOLUTION

AILEEN FISHER

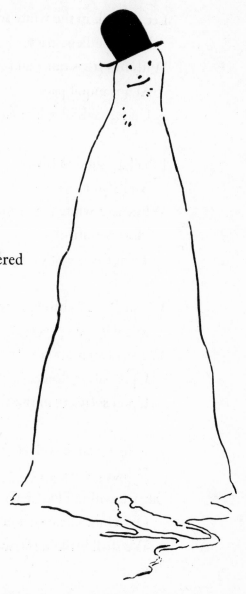

The snowman's hat was crooked
    And his nose was out of place
And several of his whiskers
    Had fallen from his face.

But the snowman didn't notice
    For he was trying to think
Of a New Year's resolution
    That wouldn't melt or shrink.

He thought and planned and pondered
    With his little snow-ball head
Till his eyes began to glisten
    And his toes began to spread;

And at last he said, "I've got it—
    I'll make a firm resolve
That no matter what the weather
    My smile will not dissolve."

Now the snowman acted wisely
    And his resolution won
For his splinter smile was *wooden*
    And it didn't mind the sun!

SPRING RAIN

HARRY BEHN

Leaves make a slow
Whispering sound
As down the drops go
Drip to the ground
   Peace, peace, says the tree.

Good wet rain!
Shout happy frogs,
Peepers and big green
Bulls in bogs,
   Lucky, lucky are we!

On a bough above,
Head under wing,
A mourning dove
Waits time to sing.
   Ah me, she sighs, ah me!

THE MORNS ARE MEEKER THAN THEY WERE

EMILY DICKINSON

The morns are meeker than they were,
The nuts are getting brown;
The berry's cheek is plumper,
The rose is out of town.

The maple wears a gayer scarf,
The field a scarlet gown.
Lest I should be old-fashioned,
I'll put a trinket on.

A SUMMER MORNING

RACHEL FIELD

I saw dawn creep across the sky,
And all the gulls go flying by.
I saw the sea put on its dress
Of blue mid-summer loveliness,
And heard the trees begin to stir
Green arms of pine and juniper.
I heard the wind call out and say:
"Get up, my dear, it is to-day!"

APRIL RAIN SONG

LANGSTON HUGHES

Let the rain kiss you
Let the rain beat upon your head with silver liquid drops.
Let the rain sing you a lullaby.

The rain makes still pools on the sidewalk.
The rain makes running pools in the gutter.
The rain plays a little sleep-song on our roof at night—

And I love the rain.

THE MIST AND ALL

DIXIE WILLSON

I like the fall,
The mist and all.
I like the night owl's
Lonely call—
And wailing sound
Of wind around.

I like the gray
November day,
And bare, dead boughs
That coldly sway
Against my pane.
I like the rain.

I like to sit
And laugh at it—
And tend
My cozy fire a bit.
I like the fall—
The mist and all.

7

just for fun

THE LOBSTER QUADRILLE

LEWIS CARROLL

"Will you walk a little faster?" said a whiting to a snail,
"There's a porpoise close behind us, and he's treading on
my tail.
See how eagerly the lobsters and the turtles all advance!
They are waiting on the shingle—will you come and join the
dance?
     Will you, won't you, will you, won't you,
       will you join the dance?
     Will you, won't you, will you, won't you,
       won't you join the dance?

"You can really have no notion how delightful it will be
When they take us up and throw us, with the lobsters
out to sea!"
But the snail replied, "Too far, too far!" and gave a look
askance—
Said he thanked the whiting kindly, but he would not join
the dance.
     Would not, could not, would not, could not,
       would not join the dance.
     Would not, could not, would not, could not,
       could not join the dance.

"What matters it how far we go?" his scaly friend replied.
"There is another shore, you know, upon the other side.

The further off from England the nearer is to France—
Then turn not pale, beloved snail, but come and join the
dance.
      Will you, won't you, will you, won't you,
        will you join the dance?
      Will you, won't you, will you, won't you,
        won't you join the dance?"

GODFREY GORDON
GUSTAVUS GORE

WILLIAM BRIGHTY RANDS

Godfrey Gordon Gustavus Gore—
No doubt you have heard the name before—
Was a boy who never would shut a door!

The wind might whistle, the wind might roar,
And teeth be aching and throats be sore,
But still he never would shut the door.

His father would beg, his mother implore,
"Godfrey Gordon Gustavus Gore,
We really *do* wish you would shut the door!"

Their hands they wrung, their hair they tore;
But Godfrey Gordon Gustavus Gore
Was deaf as the buoy out at the Nore.

When he walked forth the folks would roar,
"Godfrey Gordon Gustavus Gore,
Why don't you think to shut the door?"

They rigged out a Shutter with sail and oar,
And threatened to pack off Gustavus Gore
On a voyage of penance to Singapore.

But he begged for mercy, and said, "No more!
Pray do not send me to Singapore
On a Shutter, and then I will shut the door!"

"You will?" said his parents; "then keep on shore!
But mind you do! For the plague is sore
Of a fellow that never will shut the door,
Godfrey Gordon Gustavus Gore!"

ANTONIO

LAURA E. RICHARDS

Antonio, Antonio,
Was tired of living alonio.
   He thought he would woo
   Miss Lissamy Lu,
Miss Lissamy Lucy Molonio.

Antonio, Antonio,
Rode off on his polo-ponio.
   He found the fair maid
   In a bowery shade,
A-sitting and knitting alonio.

Antonio, Antonio,
Said, "If you will be my ownio,
    I'll love you true,
    And I'll buy for you,
An icery creamery conio!"

"Oh, *no*nio, Antonio!
You're far too bleak and bonio!
    And all that I wish,
    You singular fish,
Is that you will quickly begonio."

Antonio, Antonio,
He uttered a dismal moanio;
    Then ran off and hid
    (Or I'm told that he did)
In the Anticatarctical Zonio.

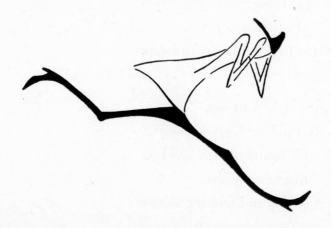

JONATHAN BING

BEATRICE CURTIS BROWN

Poor old Jonathan Bing
Went out in his carriage to visit the King,
But everyone pointed and said, "Look at that!
Jonathan Bing has forgotten his hat!"
(He'd forgotten his hat!)

Poor old Jonathan Bing
Went home and put on a new hat for the King,
But up by the palace a soldier said, "Hi!
You can't see the King; you've forgotten your tie!"
(He'd forgotten his tie!)

Poor old Jonathan Bing,
He put on a beautiful tie for the King,
But when he arrived an Archbishop said, "Ho!
You can't come to court in pyjamas, you know!"

Poor old Jonathan Bing
Went home and addressed a short note to the King:
"If you please will excuse me I won't come to tea;
For home's the best place for all people like me!"

THE OWL AND THE PUSSY-CAT

EDWARD LEAR

The Owl and the Pussy-Cat went to sea
   In a beautiful pea-green boat:
They took some honey, and plenty of money
   Wrapped up in a five-pound note.
The Owl looked up to the stars above,
   And sang to a small guitar,
"O lovely Pussy, O Pussy, my love,
   What a beautiful Pussy you are,
         You are,
         You are!
   What a beautiful Pussy you are!"

Pussy said to the Owl, "You elegant fowl,
   How charmingly sweet you sing!
Oh! let us be married; too long we have tarried:
   But what shall we do for a ring?"
They sailed away, for a year and a day,
   To the land where the bong-tree grows;
And there in a wood a Piggy-wig stood,
   With a ring at the end of his nose,
         His nose,
         His nose,
   With a ring at the end of his nose.

"Dear Pig, are you willing to sell for one shilling
  Your ring?" Said the Piggy, "I will."
So they took it away, and were married next day
  By the Turkey who lives on the hill.
They dinèd on mince and slices of quince,
  Which they ate with a runcible spoon;
And hand in hand, on the edge of the sand,
  They danced by the light of the moon,
          The moon,
          The moon,
They danced by the light of the moon.

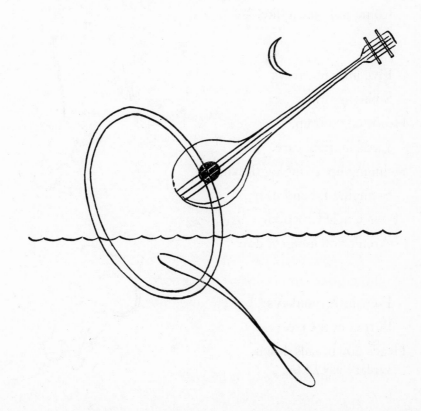

THE MONKEYS AND
THE CROCODILE

LAURA E. RICHARDS

Five little monkeys
   Swinging from a tree;
Teasing Uncle Crocodile,
   Merry as can be.
Swinging high, swinging low,
   Swinging left and right:
"Dear Uncle Crocodile,
   Come and take a bite!"

Five little monkeys
   Swinging in the air;
Heads up, tails up,
   Little do they care.
Swinging up, swinging down,
   Swinging far and near:
"Poor Uncle Crocodile,
   Aren't you hungry, dear?"

Four little monkeys
   Sitting in the tree;
Heads down, tails down,
   Dreary as can be.

Weeping loud, weeping low,
　　Crying to each other:
"Wicked Uncle Crocodile,
　　To gobble up our brother!"

THE PIRATE DON DURK
OF DOWDEE

MILDRED PLEW MEIGS

Ho, for the Pirate Don Durk of Dowdee!
He was as wicked as wicked could be,
But oh, he was perfectly gorgeous to see!
　　The Pirate Don Durk of Dowdee.

His conscience, of course, was as black as a bat,
But he had a floppety plume on his hat
And when he went walking it jiggled—like that!
　　The plume of the Pirate Dowdee.

His coat it was crimson and cut with a slash,
And often as ever he twirled his mustache
Deep down in the ocean the mermaids went splash,
　　Because of Don Durk of Dowdee.

Moreover, Dowdee had a purple tattoo,
And stuck in his belt where he buckled it through
Were a dagger, a dirk and a squizzamaroo,
　　For fierce was the Pirate Dowdee.

So fearful he was he would shoot at a puff,
And always at sea when the weather grew rough
He drank from a bottle and wrote on his cuff,
　　Did Pirate Don Durk of Dowdee.

Oh, he had a cutlass that swung at his thigh
And he had a parrot called Pepperkin Pye,
And a zigzaggy scar at the end of his eye
   Had Pirate Don Durk of Dowdee.

He kept in a cavern, this buccaneer bold,
A curious chest that was covered with mould,
And all of his pockets were jingly with gold!
   Oh jing! went the gold of Dowdee.

His conscience, of course, it was crook'd like a squash,
But both of his boots made a slickery slosh,
And he went through the world with a wonderful swash,
   Did Pirate Don Durk of Dowdee.

It's true he was wicked as wicked could be,
His sins they outnumbered a hundred and three,
But oh, he was perfectly gorgeous to see,
   The Pirate Don Durk of Dowdee.

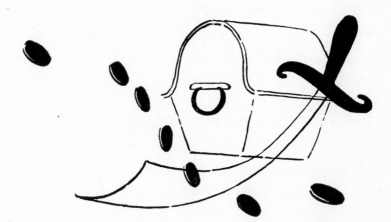

ELETELEPHONY

LAURA E. RICHARDS

Once there was an elephant,
Who tried to use the telephant—
No! no! I mean an elephone
Who tried to use the telephone—
(Dear me! I am not certain quite
That even now I've got it right.)

Howe'er it was, he got his trunk
Entangled in the telephunk;
The more he tried to get it free,
The louder buzzed the telephee—
(I fear I'd better drop the song
Of elephop and telephong!)

THE WALRUS AND
THE CARPENTER

L E W I S   C A R R O L L

The sun was shining on the sea,
    Shining with all his might:
He did his very best to make
    The billows smooth and bright—
And this was odd, because it was
    The middle of the night.

The moon was shining sulkily,
    Because she thought the sun
Had got no business to be there
    After the day was done—
"It's very rude of him," she said,
    "To come and spoil the fun!"

The sea was wet as wet could be,
    The sands were dry as dry.
You could not see a cloud, because
    No cloud was in the sky:
No birds were flying overhead—
    There were no birds to fly.

The Walrus and the Carpenter
    Were walking close at hand;

They wept like anything to see
    Such quantities of sand;
"If this were only cleared away,"
    They said, "it *would* be grand!"

"If seven maids with seven mops
    Swept it for half a year,
Do you suppose," the Walrus said,
    "That they could get it clear?"
"I doubt it," said the Carpenter,
    And shed a bitter tear.

"O Oysters, come and walk with us!"
    The Walrus did beseech.
"A pleasant walk, a pleasant talk,
    Along the briny beach:
We cannot do with more than four,
    To give a hand to each."

The eldest Oyster looked at him,
    But never a word he said:
The eldest Oyster winked his eye,
    And shook his heavy head—
Meaning to say he did not choose
    To leave the oyster-bed.

But four young Oysters hurried up,
    All eager for the treat:

Their coats were brushed, their faces washed,
  Their shoes were clean and neat—
And this was odd, because, you know,
  They hadn't any feet.

Four other Oysters followed them,
  And yet another four;
And thick and fast they came at last,
  And more, and more, and more—
All hopping through the frothy waves,
  And scrambling to the shore.

The Walrus and the Carpenter
  Walked on a mile or so,
And then they rested on a rock
  Conveniently low:
And all the little Oysters stood
  And waited in a row.

"The time has come," the Walrus said,
  "To talk of many things:
Of shoes—and ships—and sealing wax—
  Of cabbages—and kings—
And why the sea is boiling hot—
  And whether pigs have wings."

"But wait a bit," the Oysters cried,
  "Before we have our chat;

For some of us are out of breath,
    And all of us are fat!"
"No hurry!" said the Carpenter.
    They thanked him much for that.

"A loaf of bread," the Walrus said,
    "Is what we chiefly need:
Pepper and vinegar besides
    Are very good indeed—
Now if you're ready, Oysters dear,
    We can begin to feed."

"But not on us!" the Oysters cried,
    Turning a little blue.
"After such kindness, that would be
    A dismal thing to do!"
"The night is fine," the Walrus said.
    "Do you admire the view?

"It was so kind of you to come!
    And you are very nice!"
The Carpenter said nothing but
    "Cut us another slice:
I wish you were not quite so deaf—
    I've had to ask you twice!"

"It seems a shame," the Walrus said,
    "To play them such a trick.

After we've brought them out so far,
  And made them trot so quick!"
The Carpenter said nothing but
  "The butter's spread too thick!"

"I weep for you," the Walrus said:
  "I deeply sympathize."
With sobs and tears he sorted out
  Those of the largest size,
Holding his pocket-handkerchief
  Before his streaming eyes.

"O Oysters," said the Carpenter,
  "You've had a pleasant run!
Shall we be trotting home again?"
  But answer came there none—
And this was scarcely odd, because
  They'd eaten every one.

INDEX OF AUTHORS

INDEX OF TITLES

INDEX OF FIRST LINES

The sea gull curves his wings,
The sea gull turns his eyes

Up the airy mountain,
Down the rushy glen,
We daren't go a-hunting
For fear of little men

Five little monkeys
Swinging from a tree,
Teasing Uncle Crocodile,
Merry as can be

A road might lead to anywhere
To harbor towns or quay

I think mice
Are rather nice

I'm going out to clean the pasture spring,
I'll only stop to rake the leaves away

Will there really be a morning?
Is there such a thing as day?

All along the backwater,
Through the rushes tall,
Ducks are a-dabbling,
Up tails all!

She had corn flowers in her ear
As she came up the lane